MathStart®
COUNTING COINS

W9-AYA-463

The Penny Pot

by Stuart J. Murphy • illustrated by Lynne Cravath

SCHOLASTIC INC.
New York Toronto London Auckland
Sydney New Delhi Hong Kong

For Barbara Elleman—who has provided more
than a potful of friendship and support
—S.J.M.

For Leigh and Lauren
—L.C.

Bugs incorporated in the MathStart series design were painted by Jon Buller.
The illustrations for this book were done with acrylic paint on 140 lb. Arches hot press watercolor paper.

Text copyright © 1998 by Stuart J. Murphy.
Illustrations copyright © 1998 by Lynne W. Cravath.
All rights reserved. Published by Scholastic Inc., 557 Broadway, New York, NY 10012,
by arrangement with HarperCollins Children's Books.
Printed in the U.S.A.

ISBN-13: 978-0-545-26851-6
ISBN-10: 0-545-26851-6

16 17 18 19 20   40   19 18 17 16 15 14 13

It was a hot Saturday in June, and the school fair was very crowded. The busiest place of all was the face-painting booth. Fran, the art teacher, was in charge.

More than anything else, Jessie wanted to get her face painted. It cost 50 cents.

Jessie emptied her pockets and counted her money.

10 ··· 20 ··· 30 ··· 35 ··· 36 ··· 37 ··· 38 ··· **39¢**

She had three dimes, one nickel, and four pennies.

"Oh," she said sadly. "I have only 39 cents." Now
she wished she hadn't bought that ice cream cone.

7

"Don't worry," said Fran. "People will put their extra pennies in this pot, and you can have them. Wait and see."

So Jessie sat down to wait.

Soon Miguel came along. "I'd like to get my face painted," he said to Fran.

"Sure," she replied. "Do you have 50 cents?"

"Let's see," said Miguel.

25 · · · 30 · · · 40 · · · 50 · · · 51 · · · 52 · · · 53¢

He had a quarter, a nickel, two dimes, and three pennies.

"More than enough," said Fran. "Would you like to put your extra pennies into the pot for someone else to use?"

"Sure!" said Miguel.

"Now," said Fran, "what would you like to be?"
"I like clowns," said Miguel. "Can you make me into one?"
In five minutes Miguel looked like the funniest clown around.

Jessie's friend Rachel came by next, with her little sister, Sam. "I want my face painted!" cried Sam.

"Okay, okay," said Rachel. "Let's look in your purse."

25 · · · 35 · · · 40 · · · 45 · · · 46 · · · 47 · · · 48 · · · 49 · · · 50 · · · 51 · · · **52¢**

There was a quarter, a dime, two nickels, and seven pennies.

"You have enough money!" she told her. "And you even have two pennies left for the penny pot."

"What would you like to be?" Fran asked Sam.
"A star!" said Sam. "Because my mom says I'm her little star."

Fran painted a big purple star on Sam's face.
Then she added a twinkly sticker to one point,
right on Sam's forehead.

"Now I'm *really* a star!" said Sam.

The next person in line was Jonathan. "I know just how much money I have," he said. "I have 54 cents."

10 · · 20 · · 30 · · 35 · · 40 · · 45 · · · 50 · · · 51 · · 52 · · 53 · · 54¢

And sure enough, that's what he had:
three dimes, three nickels, and nine pennies.

Jonathan put the four extra pennies into the penny pot.

"And what would you like to be?" Fran asked him.

"Hmm," he said. "I don't really know. Do you have any ideas?"

"I think you'd look good as a bear," she said.

And he did, too.

After a few minutes Annie came along. "I'd like to get my face painted," she said. She put her money on the table and counted it out.

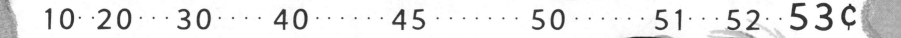

10 · 20 · · · 30 · · · · 40 · · · · · 45 · · · · · 50 · · · · · 51 · · 52 · 53¢

There were two dimes, four nickels, and thirteen pennies.

"Whew," she said. "I have enough, and even some extra pennies to put in the pot."

23

"I know just what I want to be!" Annie said before Fran could even ask. "I want to be a scary monster."

"I'll do my best," said Fran. When she was done, Annie didn't look like Annie at all.

Just when Jessie was getting very tired of waiting, Fran smiled at her. "Why don't you see what's in the penny pot now?" she said. "Maybe there will be enough, along with your 39 cents."

Jessie took all her money out of her pocket. Then she turned over the penny pot and dumped the money out onto the table.

39 · · · · · · · 40 · · · · · · · 45 · · · · · · · 50 · · · · · · · 51¢

She counted it once, and then she counted it again to be sure.

"Fifty cents!" she shouted. "Plus one cent left over!"
"You can leave that penny in the penny pot for the
next person who needs it," said Fran. "Now,
what would you like to be?"

Jessie couldn't make up her mind. A star? A bear? A clown? They were all nice, but she wanted to be something different.

All at once Fran's cat knocked over the jar of blue paint. "Scat, Chester!" said Fran, catching the jar just in time.

And then—just like that—Jessie knew what she wanted to be.

Soon all the kids from school were gathered to look at Jessie's painted face.

"That's the best one ever!" said Annie.

"I think it is," agreed Jessie. "Isn't it, Chester?"

Chester just swished his tail.

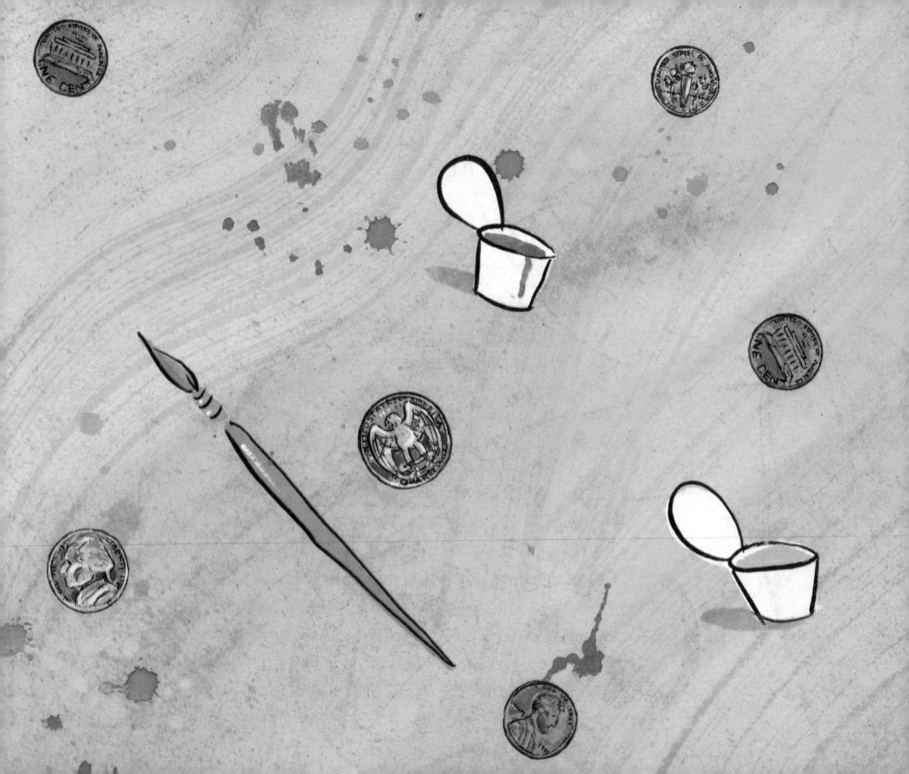